STORY TIME TWO

STORY TIME TWO

Jacqueline Sibley

Illustrated by
Jennifer Kisler

SCRIPTURE UNION
5 Wigmore Street, London W1H OAD

Contents

God's news for Mary

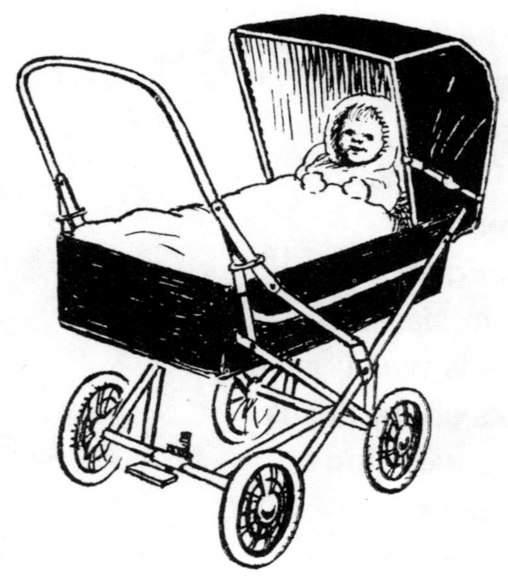

I wonder if you have a baby brother or sister in your house? I wonder if your Auntie has a baby in her house? Or I wonder if the lady next door has a baby? It's exciting when we know that a new baby is going to be born, isn't it? Sometimes we seem to wait such a long time. But there are lots of things for the

Mummy to do before her baby comes. She must have everything quite ready.

She must go to the shop to buy some baby things. She must buy nappies and pins; she must buy a pram and a cover; she must buy a bath and some soap; she must buy some tiny clothes. Can you think of some other things that she must buy?

Sometimes the Mummy does some knitting and sewing too. She knits coats and bootees for her baby. She sews dresses and nighties for her baby. She wants everything to be ready when her baby is born.

A long time ago, in a country far away, there was a lady whom God had chosen to have a very special Baby. The lady's name was Mary. Mary lived in a little house. Her house wasn't at all like your house. Her house was small and square. It had a flat roof. It had stairs outside that went up to the roof. It had only one room inside. I wonder whether you would like to have a house with only one room? You would have to play in there in the day-time and sleep there at night-time.

Mary was going to be married to a man called Joseph. Joseph was a good, kind man. He was a carpenter. A carpenter makes furniture and tools from wood. Joseph made strong wooden boxes for people to store their things in; he made cradles for the babies to sleep in; he made all kinds of things. Every day he worked very hard in his carpenter's shop. 'Zz, zz, zz' went his saw. 'Bang! Bang! Bang!' went his hammer. Mary was looking forward to the day when she would marry Joseph the carpenter.

One day when Mary was at home in her little house, God sent an angel to speak to her. The angel's name was Gabriel. We don't know what Gabriel looked like, but we do know that he had to bring a special message. God had sent Gabriel with a special message for Mary.

When Mary saw Gabriel and heard him speaking, she was frightened. But he said to her, 'Don't be afraid, Mary. God has chosen you. God says that you will have a Baby Boy. He will be a very special Baby, because He will be God's own Son. When He is born you must call Him "Jesus".'

Mary listened to the angel, Gabriel. She knew that God had promised to send a special King into the world one day. That King would be God's own Son. But she had never thought that God would choose *her* to be His mother. She was very surprised.

8

But she believed what Gabriel said. She didn't say, 'I must be dreaming, I can't believe it.' She believed that God had chosen her and she was glad. When Gabriel had gone, she sang a special song to say 'Thank You' to God for choosing her.

Then she had to get ready for the Baby. In those days, babies didn't wear nappies or

cardigans or bootees or dresses, like the babies you know. Instead they wore clothes called 'swaddling clothes.' So Mary got ready some 'swaddling clothes' for the Baby.

God had told Mary that He had chosen her to look after His Son. He had to tell Joseph the news too. So one night Joseph had a special dream. In his dream an angel spoke to him. The angel said, 'Joseph, in a little while Mary will have a Baby. Her Baby will be a very special One. He will be God's own Son. You must call him "Jesus".'

So Mary and Joseph were married and they waited for God to send His Son, just as He had promised.

A Prayer

Thank You, God, for choosing Mary and Joseph to look after Baby Jesus. Thank You for all the babies that I know. Please help their Mummies and Daddies to look after them. Amen.

Born in a stable

One day a messenger came to the town where Mary and Joseph were living. The messenger had some important news from the king. Everyone listened very carefully. He said, 'The king wants to count all the people. Everyone must go back to the town where their family used to live. Then you will all be counted.'

Mary and Joseph's family used to live in Bethlehem. So when they heard the messenger, they knew that they would have to go to Bethlehem.

They couldn't go in a comfortable bus, or on a fast train, because there weren't any buses or trains then. The rich people rode on camels or on horses. The poor people rode on donkeys or else they walked. Mary and Joseph were too poor to have a camel or a horse. They had a donkey.

It was a long way to Bethlehem. It took Mary and Joseph three days to get there. Each night they stayed at a house. Each day

Mary rode on the donkey and Joseph walked beside her. 'Clip, clop, clip, clop, clip, clop,' went the donkey's hooves as they walked along.

After three days they came to Bethlehem. Hundreds and hundreds of people were there. Everyone was waiting to be counted. Bethlehem was very crowded indeed.

'May we stop as soon as we can?' asked Mary. 'Certainly, we shall,' said Joseph. Soon they came to a house. Joseph knocked on the door. Knock! Knock! Knock! The man came out. 'Have you any room in your house?' Joseph asked. 'My wife is very tired. We should like to stay for the night.' 'No, I'm sorry, I haven't any room,' answered the man. 'You cannot stay here.' And he closed the door.

'Never mind, Mary,' said Joseph, 'we'll ask at another house.' So they walked further down the road. 'Clip, clop, clip, clop, clip, clop,' went the donkey's hooves as they walked along.

At the next house Joseph knocked on the

14

door. Knock! Knock! Knock! The man came out. 'Have you any room in your house?' Joseph asked. 'My wife is very tired. We should like to stay for the night.' 'No, I'm sorry, I haven't any room,' answered the man. 'You cannot stay here.' And he closed the door.

'Let's go a bit further,' said Joseph. Mary and Joseph were very tired. There were so many people in Bethlehem. But Joseph knew that they must find somewhere to sleep. 'I'm sure that God will help us to find somewhere,' said Mary.

Then they came to a house where lots of people could stay. Joseph knocked at the door. Knock! Knock! Knock! The man came out. 'Have you any room in your house?' Joseph asked. 'My wife is very tired. We should like to stay for the night.' 'No, I'm sorry, I haven't any room,' answered the man. 'You cannot stay in my house.' But I expect he saw Mary sitting on the donkey looking tired, because then he said, 'I haven't any room in my *house,* but there is room in my stable. The animals that belong to the other travellers are there. My cows are there too. But your wife looks very tired. You may sleep there if you like.'

So Mary and Joseph went to the stable at

the back of the house. They found a corner away from the animals, and lay down in the straw.

That night Jesus, God's Son, was born. He was God's Son, but He wasn't born in a palace or a comfortable house. He was born in a stable with animals nearby.

Mary wrapped Baby Jesus in the swaddling clothes that she had brought. But she hadn't a cradle for Him. So Joseph said, 'Let's use one of the animal's feeding boxes.' The feeding box was called a manger. Joseph put some clean straw into the manger and then Mary gently put Jesus down to sleep.

Mary and Joseph looked at Baby Jesus. They loved Him very much. They were so happy. They knew that God had sent His Son as He had promised. Jesus, God's Son, had been born.

A Prayer

Thank You, God, for keeping Your promise to send Baby Jesus to this world. Amen.

The shepherds

Once there was a shepherd. We do not know his name, but we shall call him Benjamin. Benjamin and his friends looked after some sheep

One night, they were on a hill outside Bethlehem. It was a cold night and Benjamin wrapped his cloak around himself to keep warm.

The shepherds had built a fire. The fire frightened away any lions or bears that might be around, for lions and bears like to catch little lambs. The fire also kept the shepherds warm. Benjamin lay down near it to go to sleep. He could see the stars twinkling in the sky. He could hear the sheep saying 'Baa' softly to one another.

Some other shepherds were lying near the fire too. But some stayed awake because it was their turn to look after the sheep. They had to see that none wandered away and was lost. They had to make sure that no lions or bears were around.

Suddenly Benjamin saw a light. It was shining very brightly. It was much brighter than the flickering fire or the twinkling stars. He couldn't understand what it was. He jumped up and looked around. Then he saw an angel.

He had never seen an angel before and he was frightened. He looked for his friends. They had seen the angel too. They were kneeling on the ground hiding their faces. So Benjamin knelt on the ground and hid his face. No one dared to look at the angel. They were all afraid.

The angel knew that they were frightened. He said to them, 'Don't be afraid! I have come to bring you some good news. Tonight God's Son has been born. He has been born quite near here in Bethlehem. You can find Him for yourselves. You will know when you have found Him because He has been born in a stable. His mother has put Him in a manger. She hasn't a proper cradle for Him.'

Suddenly Benjamin saw some other angels in the sky. They were singing a beautiful song to praise God. Benjamin listened to their song. He had never heard anything so beautiful before. He wondered if he were really dreaming. Then the song ended. The angels went away. The bright light disappeared. It was quiet and dark everywhere again.

Some of the shepherds rubbed their eyes. Some of them stood up. No one spoke for a little while. Then one of the older men said, 'Why are we all standing here? We must go straight to Bethlehem. We must find this Baby whom God has told us about.' 'Of course we must go,' said another shepherd. 'Yes! yes!' said Benjamin and everyone else.

So the shepherds left their sheep on the hillside. They hurried down to Bethlehem as fast as they could go. Benjamin was very

excited. He could hardly wait to get there.

Soon they came to Bethlehem and found the stable where Mary and Joseph were staying. One shepherd went quietly inside. 'May my friends and I see your Baby, please?' he asked Mary. 'Of course you may,' Mary replied. So all the shepherds looked at Baby Jesus. They were very quiet. They didn't want to frighten Him.

Benjamin looked at Him too. Baby Jesus was wrapped in swaddling clothes and lying in a manger, just as the angel had said. He was very, very tiny.

When all the shepherds had seen Him, I expect that Joseph asked them, 'How did you know that a Baby had been born?' The shepherds said, 'An angel told us.' Then they told Mary and Joseph what had happened on the hillside. Benjamin looked at Mary. She was listening very carefully to the shepherds.

But at last they had to go. One shepherd said, 'Thank you for letting us see the Baby. But we must go back to our sheep now. We have left them on the hillside.' So Benjamin and the other shepherds went back to look after their sheep.

They were all so happy that they had seen Baby Jesus. Each one of them said 'Thank You' to God for sending the angel to tell them about Him, and for letting them see Him. Benjamin said 'Thank You' to God too. He knew that he would never forget that wonderful night.

A Prayer

Dear God, I am glad that the angel told the shepherds about Baby Jesus. Thank You for the people who tell me about Him. Amen.

Saying 'Thank You'

When you were a very tiny baby, Mummy and Daddy gave you a name. They thought about lots of names. But at last they chose the one that they liked best of all and gave it to you.

When Jesus was born, Mary and Joseph didn't have to think about His name. God had already chosen it. He told Mary and Joseph that they must call the Baby 'Jesus'. So they did. They loved Jesus very much indeed. They often said 'Thank You' to God for Him.

When Jesus was about six weeks old, Joseph said to Mary, 'It's time we went to God's House to say a special "Thank You" for Jesus.' 'Yes,' said Mary, 'we must go to

the Temple.' The Temple was God's House in the big city of Jerusalem.

Early one morning Mary and Joseph set off. Mary rode on the donkey. She carried Baby Jesus very carefully in her arms. Joseph walked beside her. 'Clip, clop, clip, clop, clip, clop' went the donkey's hooves as they walked along.

At last they came to the big city of Jerusalem. There were lots of people everywhere. There were big men and little men. There were big ladies and little ladies. There were fat men and thin men. There were fat ladies and thin ladies. There were all kinds of people. They were in the streets; they were in the houses; they were in the shops. Joseph led the little donkey carefully through all these people. Soon they came to God's House.

Nearby there were some men selling animals

and birds. 'Here we are,' said Joseph. 'You wait here for a minute, while I buy two pigeons.' He bought two pigeons from one of the men. He gave them to Mary.

Mary took them with her into God's House. She took them as a present to give to God. In those days people often took presents with them into God's House. No one thought it was at all funny. It was really rather nice, wasn't it?

There was an old man in God's House. His name was Simeon. Simeon loved God very much and often talked to Him. He talked to God when he was at home. He talked to God when he was in God's House. God talked to Simeon too. He told Simeon that soon He was going to send a very special Baby to the world. The Baby would be God's own Son. God promised Simeon that he would see this Baby.

One day Simeon knew that God wanted him to go to God's House. It was the same day that Mary and Joseph went there to say 'Thank You' for Baby Jesus. Simeon saw Mary and Joseph coming in. He knew that the Baby they were bringing was the One whom God had promised to send.

Simeon walked over to Mary and Joseph and smiled. 'May I hold your little Baby?'

26

he asked. 'Of course you may,' said Mary. She carefully put Jesus into his arms. Simeon was so happy! He knew that Baby Jesus was the One whom God had promised to send. He said, 'Thank You, God, for letting me see this Baby.'

Simeon talked to Mary and Joseph and they listened to him. He told them some of the things that Jesus would do when He grew up. He said to Mary, 'This is a very precious Baby. He will help many people.'

Just then a very old lady came into the Temple. She was called Anna. Anna loved God very much. She was often in God's House. She talked to God and learned more about Him. She knew that God had promised to send a special Baby to the world. That Baby would be God's own Son.

Anna saw Mary and Joseph with Baby Jesus. She went to look at Him. She knew that Jesus was the One whom God had promised to send. She was so pleased to see Him. She said, 'Thank You, God, for letting me see this Baby.' Then she went away and told other people the Good News. She said, 'God has sent the One He promised to send.'

Mary and Joseph said 'Thank You' to God for sending Jesus. Simeon and Anna said

'Thank You' to God for sending Jesus. Boys and girls can say 'Thank You' to God for sending Jesus.

There are lots of things that you can thank God for. Think about some of them. Then say a 'Thank You' prayer.

The clever men

Have you ever stayed up late at night? Have the stars ever come out before you went to bed? The sky is dark, but the stars are bright and shiny. Have you ever seen the stars twinkling in the sky?

Long, long ago, in a country far away, there were some clever men. These men loved to look at the stars. They knew the names of all the big ones. They knew just where to look for them in the sky. They often used to look at them together.

One night when the clever men were looking at the stars the first clever man said, 'Look! There's a new star over there!' 'There can't be,' said the second clever man. 'You must have made a mistake.' 'No, he hasn't,' said the third man. 'Look! It's over there.' He pointed to the sky.

The clever men looked. They looked and they looked. And sure enough, there *was* a new star in the sky. It was big and bright and shiny. They were very excited.

They thought that the new star must be in the sky for a special reason. So they began to look in their books. They tried to find out why it was there.

They found out that God had promised to send a special King to the earth. 'The star must be shining because the new King has been born,' said the first clever man. 'He must be a very important King if there is a special star for Him,' said the second clever man. 'Let's follow the star. Let's go to see Him for ourselves,' said the third clever man. So they did.

'We must take some presents for the new King,' said the first clever man. 'We'll take some things that He can use when He is grown-up,' said the second clever man. 'Let's

take some gold, too,' said the third clever man. They chose their presents carefully. They packed them on their camels' backs. Then they climbed on to their camels' backs, too, and set off.

Camels could travel very quickly. But the clever men had a long way to go. They travelled for many, many days. All the time they followed the new star that shone in the sky.

At last they came to the country where Jesus had been born. 'A new King would be born in the big city,' they said. 'We must go there to find Him.' So they went straight there.

They said to the people, 'We are looking for the new King who has been born. Will you tell us where He is? We should like to see

Him.' But the people didn't know where the new King was.

Then, King Herod heard about the clever men. He heard that they were looking for a new King. 'He isn't in *my* palace,' he said, 'but I shall talk to my helpers. They will know where He is.' So King Herod sent for his helpers. He asked them, 'Where will the King, whom God has promised to send, be born?' The helpers said, 'God's Book says that He will be born in Bethlehem.'

Then King Herod sent a message to the clever men. He said, 'Come to my palace. Don't tell anyone that you are coming. It must be a secret.' So the clever men went to King Herod's palace. They told him all about the new star in the sky.

'Now, listen carefully to me,' said King

Herod. 'The new King has been born in Bethlehem. I want you to go there to find Him. Then I want you to come back to tell me where He is so that I can see Him too.'

So the clever men climbed on to their camels once more and set off for Bethlehem. That night they saw the new star in the sky again. They were so pleased to see it. They knew it was showing them where to go. It was shining over Bethlehem.

At last they came to the house where Mary, Joseph and Baby Jesus were staying. They had moved out of the stable where Jesus had been born. They were in a little house.

It wasn't at all like a King's house. But when the clever men went inside they knew that they had come to the right place. They saw Baby Jesus and they knew that He was the One they had been looking for. They knelt down in front of Him and gave Him their presents. They were glad that they had followed the star and seen the new King whom God had sent.

A Prayer

Dear God, I know that You helped the clever men to see Jesus. Thank You for helping me to know about Him too. Amen.

Going to Egypt

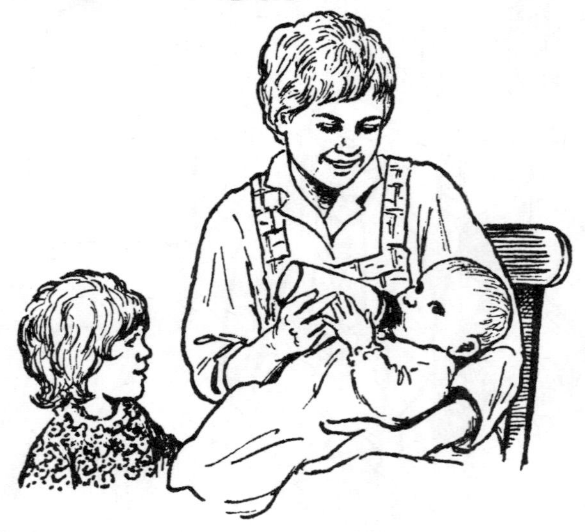

When a new baby is born, his Mummy takes great care of him, doesn't she? She feeds him, and washes him, and looks after him. When Jesus was born, Mary took great care of Him. She fed Him, and washed Him and looked after Him.

God took care of Baby Jesus too. He knew that some people were very pleased that Jesus had been born. Mary and Joseph were pleased. Simeon and Anna were pleased. The shepherds were pleased. The clever men from the country far away were pleased.

But God knew that there was one person who was not pleased. King Herod was not pleased.

King Herod was cross when the clever men told him that a new King had been born. He thought, 'I'm the king. I don't want a new king.' He was afraid that he might not be king any more.

He said to the clever men, 'I want you to go to Bethlehem to find the Baby King. Then I want you to tell me where He is, so that I can see Him too.' He didn't really want to see Him. He wanted to hurt Him. But God was taking care of Baby Jesus. He wouldn't let King Herod hurt Him.

When the clever men had seen Jesus and had given Him their presents, they said, 'We must go back to King Herod now. We must tell him where the Baby King is.' They didn't know that King Herod wanted to hurt Baby Jesus. But God was taking care of Jesus. He wouldn't let King Herod hurt Him.

That night the clever men had a special dream. In the dream God said, 'Don't go back to King Herod. Go home another way.' So they did. They didn't go back to King Herod. They didn't tell him where Baby Jesus was. God was taking care of Him.

King Herod didn't know that the clever

men had gone home. He sat in his palace and waited and waited. One day went past. Two days went past. Three days went past. Four . . . five . . . six days went past. At last King Herod grew tired of waiting. He became very cross. 'Where are those men?' he shouted. 'Why haven't they come back to tell me where the Baby is?' He grew crosser and crosser.

God knew that King Herod would be cross. But God was keeping Jesus safe. When the clever men had gone back home, Joseph had a special dream too. In the dream an angel spoke to him. The angel said, 'Get up, Joseph. Take Baby Jesus and Mary into Egypt. King Herod will soon be looking for Jesus. He wants to hurt Him.'

Joseph woke up. It was the middle of the night. It was still dark. But he woke Mary at once. He said, 'Wake up, Mary. An angel has told me that we must take Jesus to Egypt.'

Mary got up quickly, and while it was still night-time, they set off. Mary rode on the donkey. She carried Baby Jesus carefully in her arms. Joseph walked beside her. 'Clip, clop, clip, clop, clip, clop,' went the donkey's hooves as they walked along.

Soon the sun began to shine and it was

day-time. Mary and Joseph went on. They were tired but they didn't stop. They walked a long, long way. At last it began to get dark again. They came to a house where lots of people could stay. 'Let's stay here for the night,' said Mary. So they did.

The next morning they were up early. They had something to eat and then they started off again. 'Clip, clop, clip, clop, clip, clop,' went the donkey's hooves as they walked along. They walked for another day, and another day, and another day. Every day they walked and every night when it became dark they stayed at a house. At last they came to Egypt. They knew that Baby Jesus would be safe there. God was taking care of Him.

All this time King Herod was in his palace. He was still very cross. At last he sent for one of his servants. He said, 'Those men have not come back to tell me where the new King is. You must go to find Him instead.' So the servant went to Bethlehem. He looked and looked for Baby Jesus. But he couldn't find Him. He was too late! Jesus was quite safe in Egypt. And there He stayed with Mary and Joseph until King Herod died. They knew that Jesus would be safe there. God was taking care of Him.

A Prayer

Thank You, God, for taking care of Baby Jesus. Please take care of me and all the people I love. Amen.

At home in Nazareth

Mary and Joseph took Jesus to Egypt so that He would be safe from King Herod. But one day King Herod died and they didn't have to stay in Egypt any longer. It was quite safe for them to go home again.

So Mary and Joseph took Jesus to their home in Nazareth. They were pleased to be back there and to see all their friends. They had been away a long time.

Mary, Joseph and Jesus lived together in a little house. Their house wasn't at all like your house. Their house was small. It had only one room inside. I wonder whether you would like to have only one room in your house? You would have to play there in the day-time and sleep there at night-time.

Mary kept the little house clean. Each day Jesus watched her sweep the floor. Sweep, sweep, sweep. There weren't any carpets on Mary's floor. Their floor was made of dried mud.

Mary often made some bread. Jesus watched her mixing the flour and water. Stir, stir, stir. When it was cooked it tasted delicious.

Sometimes Mary mended their clothes. Jesus watched her putting patches over the holes. In and out, in and out, went her needle. Mary always had something to do.

Joseph was busy too. He worked in his carpenter's shop. He made furniture and tools from wood. He made strong wooden boxes for people to store their things in; he made cradles for the babies to sleep in; he made all kinds of things. Every day he worked very

hard. 'Zz, zz, zz' went his saw. 'Bang! Bang! Bang!' went his hammer. Joseph always had something to do. Jesus liked to watch him.

Sometimes Jesus went with Mary to the well to fetch some water. When your Mummy wants water, she turns on the tap, doesn't she? But Mary didn't have a tap in her house. When she wanted some water she had to carry her water-pot to the well.

Mary balanced the water-pot carefully on her head. She always carried it this way. So did all the other ladies in Nazareth.

At the well, Mary filled her water-pot with water. Then she carried it home again. She balanced it carefully on her head and hardly ever spilt a drop.

Often, during the day, Mary would tell Jesus a story from God's Book. Sometimes Joseph would tell Him a story from God's Book too. On the Sabbath day (that is like our Sunday), Jesus went to God's House with Mary and Joseph. In God's House He heard some more stories from God's Book. Jesus loved to hear these stories.

Mary, Joseph and Jesus had dinner at the end of the day, when Joseph had finished working in his carpenter's shop. When your Mummy cooks the dinner, I expect she uses

an electric cooker or a gas cooker. But Mary
didn't have one of these in her house. She
cooked the dinner on a little fire.

Usually Mary made a stew. She put beans
and marrows and onions and leeks into her

stew. Sometimes she put meat in as well.
But meat cost a lot of money. So Mary
couldn't afford to put meat in every day.

When Joseph came in from his carpenter's
shop, Mary took the stew-pot off the fire.
She put it on to the floor. Then Mary, Joseph

46

and Jesus sat on the floor to eat their dinner. You sit on a chair near a table, don't you? But Mary and Joseph didn't have a table and some chairs. They always sat on the floor to have their dinner. But before they began to eat Joseph would say, 'Thank You' to God for their food.

When it was bedtime Jesus couldn't go to His bedroom as you do. His house had only one room inside. So he slept in the room where He played. He slept on a mattress. Every morning he rolled up his mattress and put it away. Every evening He put it on the floor at one end of the room.

Before He went to sleep, Jesus talked to God. He thanked God for all the good things that had happened during the day. He knew that God loved Him and gave Him all the good things that He had.

Then He would lie down and go to sleep. Soon another day in Nazareth would begin.

A Prayer

Thank You, God, for the home where I live and all my favourite things. Thank You for my Mummy and Daddy who look after me. Amen.

When Jesus was twelve

I like birthdays, do you? How many have you had? It's exciting to open your presents and your cards, isn't it?

Did you know that Jesus had birthdays just as you do? Each year He grew bigger and bigger. One day He was twelve. Then Joseph said to Him, 'Now You are growing up, You may go with Your mother and me to God's House in Jerusalem.' Jesus was pleased.

He had often been to God's House in Nazareth. But He had only been to God's House in Jerusalem once before. God's House in Jerusalem was called the Temple. Mary and Joseph had taken Him to the Temple when He was a tiny Baby, but He couldn't remember that.

Joseph said, 'There are some clever teachers in God's House. When You get there, they will tell You about God.' Jesus wanted to listen to the clever teachers. He wanted to hear about God. He was glad He was going to the Temple.

Lots of people who lived near Jesus were going to the Temple too. They were all going together. The boys and girls were very excited. At last they set off.

They travelled for one day . . . two days . . . three days. At last they came to Jerusalem where the Temple was. There were crowds of people everywhere.

Jesus liked to watch the people. He liked to see all the interesting places in Jerusalem as well. But most of all He liked to go to God's House, the Temple. He liked to listen to the clever teachers as they talked about God.

The days went quickly past. Soon it was time to go home again. Mary and Joseph set off with the crowd of people. They couldn't

see Jesus, but they thought that He was
playing with His friends.

At the end of the day everyone stopped.
Mary and Joseph waited for Jesus. They
waited and waited. But Jesus didn't come.
Mary was worried. 'Don't worry,' said Joseph,
'I'll look for Him.'

Joseph went to their friends. 'Have you
seen Jesus today?' he asked. 'No, we haven't
seen Him all day,' they said. Joseph went to
some more friends. 'Have you seen Jesus

today?' he asked. 'No, we haven't seen Him all day,' they said. Joseph asked more and more people, 'Have you seen Jesus today?' Everybody said the same thing, 'No, we haven't seen Him all day.'

Joseph went back to Mary. He said, 'Nobody has seen Him today. He must still be in Jerusalem.' 'Oh, dear!' said Mary, 'I do hope that He's all right.' 'He'll be all right,' Joseph said. 'Don't worry, Mary. Tomorrow we'll go back to Jerusalem to find Him.'

Early the next morning Mary and Joseph set off. It took them all day to go back to Jerusalem. It was nearly dark when they arrived. They went straight to their friends. 'Have you seen Jesus?' they asked. 'No, we haven't seen Him all day,' they said.

Joseph said, 'We can't look very far tonight, Mary. It's too dark. Tomorrow we'll get up early and look.' So early the next morning Mary and Joseph began to look for Jesus. 'Let's look in God's House,' said Mary. So they went to God's House, the Temple.

There were still lots of people in the Temple. In one place some people were sitting on the floor. They were listening to the clever teachers. Some of them were asking questions and the clever teachers were answering them.

Jesus was sitting in the middle of the people. He was listening to everything very carefully. Sometimes He asked the clever teachers a question. They were very surprised at the things He asked. They said to one another, 'He's a clever Boy. He knows lots of things that are in God's Book. He's asking sensible questions.'

Jesus was so interested in everything. He didn't see Mary and Joseph. But they saw Him. Mary said to Him, 'We have been looking everywhere for You, Jesus. We were very worried.'

Jesus was surprised. He said, 'Why did you worry? Didn't you know that I should be in my Father's House?' Jesus thought that Mary and Joseph would know that He was in God's House.

But Jesus could see that Mary and Joseph wanted to go home. So He said, 'Good-bye' to the clever teachers and went back to Nazareth. He hoped that next year He would be able to go to the Temple again.

A Prayer

Dear God, I am glad that on Sundays I can go to Your House or to Sunday School. Please help me to learn more about You and the things that You want me to do. Amen.

'Is the visitor as old as Daddy? Or is he even older?' I am sure Mummy and Daddy are specially careful to explain who it is who's coming.

Many years ago, when Jesus came to this world, God wanted everything to be ready for Him. God wanted people to know who He was, and to be ready to listen to Him. So He sent a man to tell people who Jesus was, and to help them to get ready to listen. The man's name was John.

John wasn't a rich man. He didn't have beautiful clothes to wear. He didn't have lovely food to eat. He didn't have a big house to live in. But lots of people came from all sorts of places to hear what he had to say, and John talked to them all.

He talked to Mummies and Daddies; he talked to Aunties and Uncles; he talked to Grandmas and Grandpas. He talked to rich men and poor men. He talked to clever men and men who were not quite so clever. He talked to shepherds. He talked to shopkeepers. He talked to soldiers.

John said to them, 'You have done some bad things. You have made God sad. You must tell Him that you are sorry.' All the people listened. When they heard what John was saying, some of them were sad. 'We are sorry that we have done bad things,' they thought. So they told God that they were sorry and they asked Him to help them not to do bad things any more.

Then John told the people about Jesus. He said, 'I have told you some things about God. But Someone else, who is a much greater Person than I am, is coming. He is God's Son. He knows just what God is like and He will teach you all about Him.' The people were glad when John said, 'God's Son will teach you more about God.' They wanted to learn more about God. John was helping them to get ready to listen to Jesus, wasn't he?

One day, John saw Jesus walking towards him. Jesus had grown up now, and John knew that soon He would begin to teach the people about God. He said to the people, 'This is the One I was talking about. He is a much greater person than I am. He is God's Son.' The people looked at Jesus. They thought, 'Now we know who John was talking about.' And some people thought 'We must listen to Him.' They were ready to listen to Jesus, weren't they?

The next day, John was standing with two of his friends. One of them was called

Andrew. Andrew and the other friend had often heard John talking about Jesus. They were ready to listen to Jesus. As they were standing together, John saw Jesus again. He said to his friends, 'There is the One whom God has sent.' So the friends left John and went to stay with Jesus for the day. John didn't mind. He was glad that his friends were ready to listen to Jesus.

Jesus knew that John had helped Andrew and his friend to know who He was and to get ready to listen to Him. He knew that John had helped some other people to know who He was, and get ready to listen to Him, too, and soon after this He began to teach the people. Lots of people came from all sorts of places to hear what Jesus had to say. I expect that some of them thought, 'This is the Person that John told us about. We must listen carefully to Him.'

John really had done just what God wanted him to do, hadn't he? He had helped the people to get ready to listen to Jesus.

A Prayer

Dear God, I know that a long time ago John told the people about Jesus. I know that today some people are telling others about Jesus too. Please help them as they work for you and help the people to listen to them. Amen.

Jesus at a wedding

Have you ever been to a wedding? Have you ever seen a bride wearing a long white dress? Perhaps she had some bridesmaids too. Maybe you have even been to a party after a wedding and had some good things to eat. People are happy at a wedding, aren't they?

Once Jesus went to a wedding. He went with His mother and some of His friends. Can you remember His mother's name? Her name was Mary. Mary, Jesus and His friends walked together to the house of the man who was being married. He was called the bridegroom.

They were hot and dusty when they arrived. But near the door there were some water-pots. Can you see them in the picture? How many are there? Let's count them. One, two, three, four, five, six. Six water-pots. They were very big. They were almost as big as you are.

A helper poured out some water from one of them. So Mary, Jesus and His friends washed their dusty feet. They felt much cooler and fresher after this. They washed their hands too. Then they went in to the wedding.

They saw the bride and bridegroom. The bride wasn't wearing a long white dress. She was wearing a pretty dress with a lovely pattern sewn on it.

There were a lot of people at the wedding party. They were talking and laughing together. The helpers were very busy. There was some lovely food for the people to eat and the helpers had to give it to them. There was some wine for the people to drink and the helpers had to pour it out for them. They had to see that everyone had what they wanted. After a while Mary saw that some of the helpers were looking worried. She saw some of them whispering together. She thought, 'Something must be wrong.' So she asked one of them, 'What's the matter?'

The helper looked sad. He said very quietly, 'We haven't enough wine. It's almost gone and we can't get any more. Soon we shall have nothing for the people to drink.' The helpers didn't know what to do.

But Mary knew what to do. She went straight to Jesus. She said to Him, 'There's no wine left. The helpers are very worried. They don't know what to do.' She knew that Jesus would help them.

Then Mary said to the helpers, 'Do what Jesus tells you to do. Everything will be all right.' The helpers believed her. They believed that Jesus would help them.

Jesus looked at the water-pots that were near the door. Can you remember how many there were? Let's count them again. One, two, three, four, five, six. Six water-pots. They were very big. They were almost as big as you are.

Jesus said to the helpers, 'Fill the water-pots

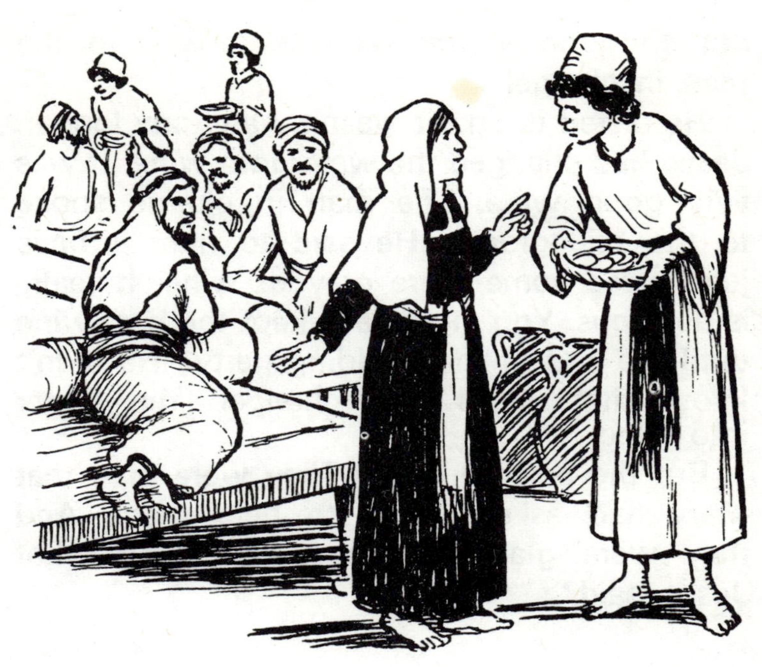

with water.' So they did. They knew that they must do what Jesus told them. They filled the big water-pots right up to the top.

Then Jesus said to them, 'Now pour some out and take it to the man in charge of the wedding party.' So they did. They didn't say, 'But this is water, we can't take water to the man in charge.' They knew that they must do what Jesus told them. They poured some out and one of the servants took it to the man in charge.

He tasted it, and it wasn't water any longer. Jesus had changed the water into wine. It was very good wine. The man in charge spoke to the bridegroom. He said to him, 'I have just tasted some more of your wine. It really is delicious. You must have kept the best wine until the end of the wedding party.' He didn't know that Jesus had changed the water into wine.

But the helpers knew. They were glad that Mary had asked Jesus to help them. And they were glad that they had done what Jesus said.

A Prayer

Dear God, I'm glad that the helpers did what Jesus told them to do, so that everyone had a happy time at the wedding. Please help me to do what Jesus wants me to do too. Amen.

The first helpers

Do you remember Andrew? He was John's friend who spent the day with Jesus. We don't know just what they said to one another. But they had a lovely day together.

At the end of the day, Andrew went to find his brother, Simon. Andrew said to Simon, 'I've had a lovely day. I've been talking to Jesus. He is the One whom God has sent. You must meet Jesus too.' So Andrew took Simon to meet Jesus.

Simon and Andrew were fishermen. Each night they went out on the lake in their boat. Each night they let down their big fishing nets into the water. Each night they waited quietly for some fish to swim into their nets. Each night they pulled up the nets again, carefully, carefully. Sometimes there were lots of fish in their nets. Sometimes there were no fish at all.

Simon and Andrew had two friends. Their names were James and John. James and John had met Jesus too. They knew that He was the One whom God had sent.

James and John were fishermen. Each night they went out on to the lake in their boat. Each night they let down their big fishing nets into the water. Each night they waited quietly for some fish to swim into their nets. Each night they pulled up the nets again, carefully, carefully. Sometimes there were lots of fish in their nets. Sometimes there were no fish at all.

Each morning Simon, Andrew, James and John took their boats back to the shore. They unloaded the fish they had caught. Then they looked carefully at their nets. They had to be sure that they were clean. They had to be sure that there were no big holes in them or else the fish would swim through again.

One night they worked very hard, but they didn't catch any fish at all. In the morning they went back to the shore and began to wash their nets. Then Jesus came by. There were a lot of people following Jesus. They wanted to listen to the stories that He told.

Jesus saw Simon, Andrew, James and John. He said to Simon, 'May I get in to your boat, please?' 'Of course You may,' said Simon. Then Jesus said, 'Go out just a little way from the shore.' So Simon did.

Jesus sat down in Simon's boat. He began to talk to the people. He told them about God and His love for them. The people listened very carefully. Simon, Andrew, James and John listened very carefully too.

When Jesus had finished speaking, He said to Simon, 'Take your boat further out to the deep water.' So Simon did. Then Jesus said, 'Let your nets down into the water

to catch some fish.' But Simon said, 'Master we were working here all night and we didn't catch anything. But if You say so I will let the nets down again.' So Simon and Andrew let the nets down into the water.

They waited quietly. Then they pulled the nets up again, carefully, carefully. What a surprise they had! The nets were full of fish. The nets were so full that they began to break. So Simon and Andrew called James and John to help them. They came quickly and soon both little boats were full of fish. The fishermen had caught lots of fish.

But then Jesus told Simon that He had another job for him to do. He said, 'From now on I want you to help Me to teach the people about God. I want you to come with Me and be My helper.'

Simon, Andrew, James and John were sure that Jesus was the One whom God had sent. They all wanted to be with Him and help Him.

They took their boats back to the shore. They unloaded all the fish that they had caught. They looked carefully at their nets, and put them away. Then they left their boats and went with Jesus. They wanted to help Him to teach the people about God.

A Prayer

Thank You, Lord Jesus, for choosing some men to help You. Please make me a helper too. Show me how I can help other people. Amen.

An unhappy man

The little boy in this picture has the measles.
He has spots on his hands, spots on his face,
spots on his tummy, spots all over him.
The doctor has seen him. He has given him
some medicine. He said, 'Drink this up and
soon you'll be better.' Have you ever been ill
in bed like this little boy?

Once, a long time ago, there was a man
who was ill. We don't know his name, but
we'll call him Mr. Reuben. Mr. Reuben didn't
have the measles, but he did have some
spots on him and his hands wouldn't work
properly.

He wasn't in bed, like the little boy in the
picture. He didn't have any medicine to take
either. The doctor had seen him, but he had
said, 'I'm sorry, Mr. Reuben. I can't make
you better. I haven't any medicine that will

make your spots go away, and make your hands work properly again.' Poor Mr. Reuben! He felt very, very unhappy.

The people who lived near Mr. Reuben found out that he was ill. They said, 'You must go away. You can't live near us any more. We might get your spots too. Go away. Go away.' So Mr. Reuben had to leave his

home and go away. Poor Mr. Reuben! He felt very, very unhappy.

Nobody wanted him to live near them. They were all afraid that they would get his spots and be ill too. Everybody said, 'You must go away. You can't live near us. You might make us ill too. Go away! Go away!' So Mr. Reuben had to keep right away from all the people. Poor Mr. Reuben! He felt very, very unhappy.

He couldn't go to work, and he didn't have any money to buy food. So the people said, 'We will leave some food for you. But you must only fetch it when we are not there. We don't want to get all those spots.'

When Mr. Reuben went to get the food he had to ring a little bell. 'Ting-a-ling-a-ling.' He had to call out, 'Keep away! Keep away!' Then the people knew that he was there and they kept away from him. Poor Mr. Reuben! He was very, very unhappy.

But one day Mr. Reuben heard about Jesus. He heard that people who were ill had gone to Jesus and that Jesus had made them better. 'I wonder if Jesus would make me better?' he thought. Then he thought, 'I don't suppose that Jesus would help me. He won't want to come near me. He might get my spots too.'

But Mr. Reuben thought and thought about Jesus. And the more he thought about Him, the more he wanted to be made better. 'I *will* ask Jesus to help me,' he thought.

And one day Jesus came by with just a few of His friends.

Mr. Reuben ran up and knelt in front of Him. He said to Jesus, 'Please will you make me better? I know that You can if You will.' He thought, 'I hope that Jesus will help me. I hope that He won't be cross because I haven't rung my bell and kept away from Him.'

Jesus looked at Mr. Reuben. He felt so sorry for him. At once He put out His hand and touched him. Then He said, 'Of course I will help you. You are better now.' Mr. Reuben looked. His spots had gone. He could use his hands again. He really was better. He said, 'Thank You, Jesus. Thank You for making me better.' He wasn't unhappy any longer. Instead he was very, very happy.

Jesus said to him, 'Now you can go home again. But first you must go to God's House to say 'Thank You' to God. Then the men there will give you a letter to tell the people that you are really better.'

So Mr. Reuben ran off to God's House. He was very, very happy. He didn't have to ring his bell, 'Ting-a-ling-a-ling,' any more. He didn't have to call out any more, 'Keep away! Keep away!' He could live in his own house again and the people wouldn't send

him away. He was so glad that Jesus had made him better.

Have you any friends who aren't feeling well and who are at home in bed? Think about them. Then say a prayer and ask God to make them better.

Matthew, the cheat

Once there was a very rich man. His name was Matthew. Matthew lived in a big house. He had beautiful clothes to wear. He had lovely food to eat. He had some helpers to look after him.

Matthew used to collect money for the king. Each morning he left his big house and went down to the road near the sea. He had a special place there. He used to sit at a table and collect money from the people who came by.

All kinds of people came by. One day a man with a donkey and cart came by. Matthew said to him, 'You must pay some money to the king because you have a donkey and cart. You can pay three silver coins.'

So the man had to pay three silver coins. He didn't want to give the money to Matthew, but he knew that he would get into trouble if he didn't. When the man had gone, Matthew put two silver coins away for the king and one silver coin into a box for himself. 'Good,' he thought, 'that's more money for me.' What a cheat Matthew was!

Another day a man who was carrying a heavy bag came by. 'Let me see what's in your bag,' Matthew said to him. The man opened his bag. Inside there were some bowls and dishes that cost a lot of money. 'You must pay the king two silver coins because you have those pots,' said Matthew.

So the man had to pay two silver coins. He didn't want to give the money to Matthew but he knew that he would get into trouble if he didn't. When the man had gone, Matthew put one silver coin away for the king, and one silver coin into a box for himself. 'Good,' he thought, 'that's more money for me.' What a cheat Matthew was!

Every day he stopped lots of people and asked them for money. None of them wanted to give the money to Matthew, but they all knew that they would get into trouble if they didn't. He always put some money away for the king and some money into a box for himself. 'Good,' he thought, 'that's more money for me.' What a cheat Matthew was!

Everybody knew that he was a cheat. Everybody knew that he took too much money from the people and kept some for himself. So not many people liked Matthew.

Some days Jesus walked along the road near the sea. Then Matthew would see Him. Some days Jesus stood quite close to Matthew and talked to the people. Then Matthew could hear what Jesus was saying. He listened to the stories that Jesus told. He didn't forget them. When he was back in his big house he thought about them.

Matthew liked Jesus. He knew that Jesus was good and kind. He knew that Jesus never

cheated people. Jesus helped people and was their Friend. 'I wish that Jesus were my Friend,' he thought. But then he felt sad. 'Jesus wouldn't be my Friend. I've cheated people and been unkind. He wouldn't like me,' he thought.

But one day Jesus came by again. He knew that Matthew had been listening to His stories and wanted to be His friend. So He stopped by Matthew's table. He looked at him and said, 'Come with Me and be one of My helpers.'

Matthew could hardly believe his ears. 'Is Jesus really asking me to be one of His helpers?' he thought. He knew that if he went with Jesus he wouldn't have time to collect money for the king. He knew that he would have to stop cheating. He knew that he wouldn't have lots of money to buy lovely food and fine clothes. But he didn't mind.

As soon as Jesus spoke to him, Matthew knew what he would do. He stood up, left his table and went with Jesus. He didn't want to cheat people any more. He wanted to help Jesus instead.

I expect that you have sometimes done some bad things. Say a prayer to tell Jesus that you are sorry.

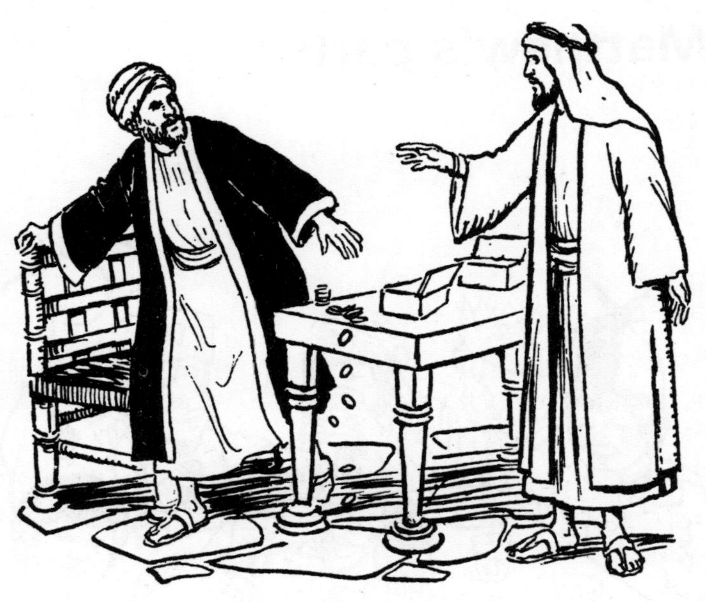

You could also say this little prayer to ask Jesus to help you to be kind and good.

A Prayer

Lord Jesus, sometimes I want to do bad things. Please help me not to do them. Please help me to be kind and good instead. Amen.

Matthew's party

Parties are fun, aren't they? We have jelly and ice-cream and cakes with icing. We play lovely games with balloons and sometimes wear fancy paper hats. I like parties, don't you?

One day Matthew had a party. It was a

grown-up party, so although they had lovely food to eat, they didn't play games as you do. Matthew had the party so that his old friends could meet his new Friend, Jesus. The people he asked to his party didn't have many friends. Matthew wanted them to know that Jesus would be their Friend, if they wanted Him to be.

On the party day, Jesus went to Matthew's house. Jesus' helpers went with Him. There were already lots of people there. Some of the people had done bad things. Some of them had been unkind to other people. Some of them collected money for the king, as Matthew used to do. They put some of the money away for the king and some of the money into a box for themselves. What cheats they were! All these people were at the party, because Matthew wanted them to meet his new Friend Jesus.

Everyone sat around the table. Matthew's helpers were very busy giving them lovely food to eat and pouring out wine for them to drink. Jesus was sitting with all the people who had done bad things. He was talking to them and they were talking to Him. Matthew was glad that his old friends could meet his new Friend Jesus.

Nearby there were some grumpy men. They saw that Jesus was inside the house. They saw that He was at a party with the people who had done bad things. They said to one another, 'Fancy Jesus going to a party with *those* people. They're bad people.'

The grumpy men thought that they were very good people. They always went to church and kept all the rules. They thought that they were very good and very much better than the other people. They wouldn't even speak to the people who had done bad things. They couldn't understand why Jesus was at a party with them.

Then they saw some of Jesus' helpers. So they said to them, 'Fancy Jesus going to a party with *those* people. They're bad people. Why is He sitting down and eating with them?'

The grumpy men didn't think that Jesus would hear them. But Jesus did hear what they were saying, and He spoke to them. He said, 'I am like a doctor. A doctor doesn't help people who are well. He helps people who are ill. He makes them better. I have come to help people who have done bad things and people who are unhappy. I have come to help them to learn about God and to do good things.'

The grumpy men listened. They knew that at the party there were people who had done bad things and people who were unhappy. So they knew that Jesus was at the party to help them. But they still thought, 'Fancy Jesus going to a party with *those* people. They're bad people.' And they went away.

But Jesus stayed at the party. He stayed to talk to the people who had done bad things. He showed them that He would help them to do good things. He stayed to talk to the people who didn't have many friends. He showed them that He would be their Friend. He loved them, just as He loved Matthew.

Jesus talked to Matthew's old friends, and Matthew listened. He was glad that Jesus had asked him to be one of His helpers. He was glad that at his party, his old friends could meet Jesus, the best Friend of all.

A Prayer

Dear Lord Jesus, I know that You are the best Friend of all. Please help my cousins and my friends to know this too. Then they can ask You to be their Friend as well. Amen.